JUSTSAYING

All About *Everybody*

IN AND OUT OF SCHOOL

THIS BOOK BELONGS TO:

Printed in South Korea by Yangjisa Co. Ltd.

First Edition, 2012.

ISBN: 978-1-909419-03-2

Published by The Red Cherry Trading Company Ltd
trading as Red Cherry Publishing.

All About Everybody™ is trademark of The Red Cherry Trading Company Ltd.
Designed by The Red Cherry Trading Company Limited and Megan Claire.
Illustrations by Megan Claire.

www.allabouteverybody.com

All About *Everybody* IN AND OUT OF SCHOOL

RED CHERRY
PUBLISHING

WHAT IS ALL ABOUT EVERYBODY?

Welcome to 'All About Everybody In and Out of School', the book that lets you find out lots of things about your friends including what they really think about school, life and everything!!

You can enjoy creating your own time capsule and make it your own special book by using the blank pages to add photos, drawings, words or doodles ......whatever you and your friends fancy!

Getting started:
Fill in your own set of questions at the beginning of the book and then simply ask your friends to complete one double page of questions and the rest is up to them! You might want to pass the book around at a special event or you may prefer to get them to complete it throughout your school years.

Enjoy getting to know your friends even better and capturing your favourite and most amusing memories of your friends both in and out of school.

All About ~~Everybody~~ MYSELF

Five words to describe me best...

My hobbies and interests are...

When I am an adult I want to be...

If I could have anything in the world it would be...

I can't live without...

If I could be invisible for a day, I would...

The silliest thing I've ever done is...

What I like most about school...

My best ever school trip and why...

My best school year memories so far are...

The best time with my friends is/was...

I can't wait to...

The hardest thing I have ever done is...

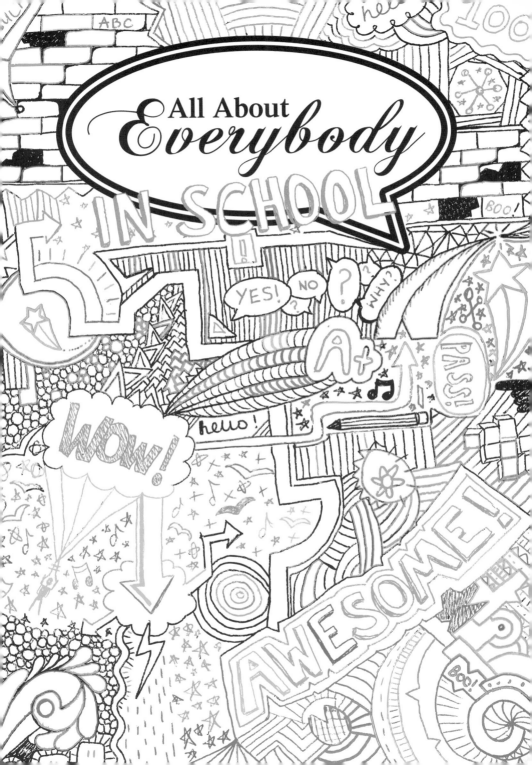

Name: _____

Today's Date: _____

Date of Birth: _____

What 5 words describe you best?

What is your hobby or interest?

What do you want to be when you are an adult?

If you could have anything in the world what would it be?

What are the things you can't live without?

If you could be invisible for a day, what would you do?

What is the silliest thing you have ever done?

What do you like most about school?

What was your best ever school trip and why?

Your best school year memories so far are...

The best time with your friends is/was...

What can't you wait to do?

Favourite TV show?

Favourite food?

Favourite subject?

Favourite teacher?

Favourite video game?

Name: _____

Today's Date: _____

Date of Birth: _____

What 5 words describe you best?

What is your hobby or interest?

What do you want to be when you are an adult?

If you could have anything in the world what would it be?

What are the things you can't live without?

If you could be invisible for a day, what would you do?

What is the silliest thing you have ever done?

What do you like most about school?

What was your best ever school trip and why?

Your best school year memories so far are...

The best time with your friends is/was...

What can't you wait to do?

Favourite TV show?

Favourite food?

Favourite subject?

Favourite teacher?

Favourite video game?

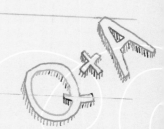

“ To the headteacher's office. ”

Name:

Today's Date:

Date of Birth:

What 5 words describe you best?

What is your hobby or interest?

What do you want to be when you are an adult?

If you could have anything in the world what would it be?

What are the things you can't live without?

If you could be invisible for a day, what would you do?

What is the silliest thing you have ever done?

What do you like most about school?

What was your best ever school trip and why?

Your best school year memories so far are...

The best time with your friends is/was...

What can't you wait to do?

Favourite TV show?

Favourite food?

Favourite subject?

Favourite teacher?

Favourite video game?

Name:

Today's Date:

Date of Birth:

What 5 words describe you best?

What is your hobby or interest?

What do you want to be when you are an adult?

If you could have anything in the world what would it be?

What are the things you can't live without?

If you could be invisible for a day, what would you do?

What is the silliest thing you have ever done?

What do you like most about school?

What was your best ever school trip and why?

Your best school year memories so far are...

The best time with your friends is/was...

What can't you wait to do?

Favourite TV show?

Favourite food?

Favourite subject?

Favourite teacher?

Favourite video game?

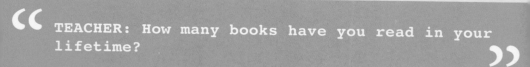
TEACHER: How many books have you read in your lifetime?

" PUPIL: I don't know. I'm not dead yet. **"**

Name: _____

Today's Date: _____

Date of Birth: _____

What 5 words describe you best?

What is your hobby or interest?

What do you want to be when you are an adult?

If you could have anything in the world what would it be?

What are the things you can't live without?

If you could be invisible for a day, what would you do?

ABC

HIGH five!

What is the silliest thing you have ever done?

What do you like most about school?

What was your best ever school trip and why?

Your best school year memories so far are...

The best time with your friends is/was...

What can't you wait to do?

Favourite TV show?

Favourite food?

Favourite subject?

Favourite teacher?

Favourite video game?

Name:

Today's Date:

Date of Birth:

What 5 words describe you best?

What is your hobby or interest?

What do you want to be when you are an adult?

If you could have anything in the world what would it be?

What are the things you can't live without?

If you could be invisible for a day, what would you do?

What is the silliest thing you have ever done?

What do you like most about school?

What was your best ever school trip and why?

WOO HOO!

Your best school year memories so far are...

The best time with your friends is/was...

What can't you wait to do?

Favourite TV show?

Favourite food?

Favourite subject?

Favourite teacher?

Favourite video game?

1

DREAM

Name:

Today's Date:

Date of Birth:

What 5 words describe you best?

What is your hobby or interest?

What do you want to be when you are an adult?

If you could have anything in the world what would it be?

What are the things you can't live without?

If you could be invisible for a day, what would you do?

What is the silliest thing you have ever done?

What do you like most about school?

What was your best ever school trip and why?

Your best school year memories so far are...

The best time with your friends is/was...

What can't you wait to do?

Favourite TV show?

Favourite food?

Favourite subject?

Favourite teacher?

Favourite video game?

Name: _____

Today's Date: _____

Date of Birth: _____

What 5 words describe you best?

What is your hobby or interest?

What do you want to be when you are an adult?

If you could have anything in the world what would it be?

What are the things you can't live without?

If you could be invisible for a day, what would you do?

What is the silliest thing you have ever done?

What do you like most about school?

What was your best ever school trip and why?

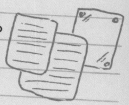

Your best school year memories so far are...

The best time with your friends is/was...

What can't you wait to do?

Favourite TV show?

Favourite food?

Favourite subject?

Favourite teacher?

Favourite video game?

" PUPIL: Not very much! **"**

Name:

Today's Date:

Date of Birth:

What 5 words describe you best?

YAY!

What is your hobby or interest?

What do you want to be when you are an adult?

If you could have anything in the world what would it be?

What are the things you can't live without?

If you could be invisible for a day, what would you do?

What is the silliest thing you have ever done?

What do you like most about school?

What was your best ever school trip and why?

Your best school year memories so far are...

The best time with your friends is/was...

What can't you wait to do?

Favourite TV show?

Favourite food?

Favourite subject?

Favourite teacher?

Favourite video game?

Name:

Today's Date:

Date of Birth:

What 5 words describe you best? *five!*

What is your hobby or interest?

What do you want to be when you are an adult?

If you could have anything in the world what would it be?

What are the things you can't live without?

If you could be invisible for a day, what would you do?

What is the silliest thing you have ever done?

What do you like most about school?

What was your best ever school trip
and why?

Your best school year memories so far are...

The best time with your friends is/was...

What can't you wait to do?

Favourite TV show?

Favourite food?

Favourite subject?

Favourite teacher?

Favourite video game?

A+

Name:

Today's Date:

Date of Birth:

What 5 words describe you best?

What is your hobby or interest?

What do you want to be when you are an adult?

If you could have anything in the world what would it be?

What are the things you can't live without?

If you could be invisible for a day, what would you do?

What is the silliest thing you have ever done?

What do you like most about school?

What was your best ever school trip
and why?

Your best school year memories so far are...

The best time with your friends is/was...

What can't you wait to do?

Favourite TV show?

Favourite food?

Favourite subject?

Favourite teacher?

Favourite video game?

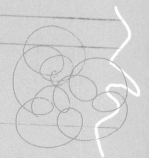

Name:

Today's Date:

Date of Birth:

What 5 words describe you best?

What is your hobby or interest?

What do you want to be when you are an adult?

If you could have anything in the world what would it be?

What are the things you can't live without?

If you could be invisible for a day, what would you do?

What is the silliest thing you have ever done?

What do you like most about school?

What was your best ever school trip and why?

Your best school year memories so far are...

The best time with your friends is/was...

What can't you wait to do?

Favourite TV show?

Favourite food?

Favourite subject?

Favourite teacher?

Favourite video game?

Why did the music teacher need a ladder?

ABC
123

" To reach the high notes. **"**

Name:

Today's Date:

Date of Birth:

What 5 words describe you best?

What is your hobby or interest?

GENIUS!

What do you want to be when you are an adult?

If you could have anything in the world what would it be?

What are the things you can't live without?

If you could be invisible for a day, what would you do?

What is the silliest thing you have ever done?

What do you like most about school?

What was your best ever school trip and why?

Your best school year memories so far are...

The best time with your friends is/was...

What can't you wait to do?

Favourite TV show?

Favourite food?

Favourite subject?

Favourite teacher?

Favourite video game?

Name:

Today's Date:

Date of Birth:

What 5 words describe you best?

#

What is your hobby or interest?

What do you want to be when you are an adult?

If you could have anything in the world what would it be?

What are the things you can't live without?

If you could be invisible for a day, what would you do?

WOO HOO!

What is the silliest thing you have ever done?

What do you like most about school?

What was your best ever school trip and why?

Your best school year memories so far are...

The best time with your friends is/was...

What can't you wait to do?

Favourite TV show?

Favourite food?

Favourite subject?

Favourite teacher?

Favourite video game?

Name:

Today's Date:

Date of Birth:

What 5 words describe you best?

What is your hobby or interest?

What do you want to be when you are an adult?

If you could have anything in the world what would it be?

What are the things you can't live without?

If you could be invisible for a day, what would you do?

What is the silliest thing you have ever done?

What do you like most about school?

What was your best ever school trip
and why?

Your best school year memories so far are...

The best time with your friends is/was...

What can't you wait to do?

Favourite TV show?

Favourite food?

Favourite subject?

Favourite teacher?

Favourite video game?

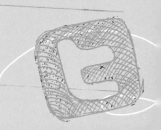

Name:

Today's Date:

Date of Birth:

What 5 words describe you best?

What is your hobby or interest?

What do you want to be when you are an adult?

If you could have anything in the world what would it be?

What are the things you can't live without?

If you could be invisible for a day, what would you do?

What is the silliest thing you have ever done?

What do you like most about school?

What was your best ever school trip and why?

Your best school year memories so far are...

The best time with your friends is/was...

What can't you wait to do?

Favourite TV show?

Favourite food?

Favourite subject?

Favourite teacher?

Favourite video game?

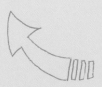

Name:

Today's Date:

Date of Birth:

What 5 words describe you best?

What is your hobby or interest?

What do you want to be when you are an adult?

If you could have anything in the world what would it be?

What are the things you can't live without?

If you could be invisible for a day, what would you do?

HI!

What is the silliest thing you have ever done?

What do you like most about school?

What was your best ever school trip and why?

Your best school year memories so far are...

The best time with your friends is/was...

What can't you wait to do?

Favourite TV show?

Favourite food?

Favourite subject?

Favourite teacher?

Favourite video game?

Name:

Today's Date:

Date of Birth:

What 5 words describe you best?

What is your hobby or interest?

What do you want to be when you are an adult?

If you could have anything in the world what would it be?

What are the things you can't live without?

If you could be invisible for a day, what would you do?

ABC

123

What is the silliest thing you have ever done?

What do you like most about school?

What was your best ever school trip and why?

Your best school year memories so far are...

The best time with your friends is/was...

What can't you wait to do?

Favourite TV show?

Favourite food?

Favourite subject?

Favourite teacher?

Favourite video game?

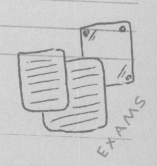

EXAMS

Name:

Today's Date:

Date of Birth:

What 5 words describe you best?

What is your hobby or interest?

What do you want to be when you are an adult?

If you could have anything in the world what would it be?

What are the things you can't live without?

If you could be invisible for a day, what would you do?

What is the silliest thing you have ever done?

What do you like most about school?

What was your best ever school trip and why?

Your best school year memories so far are...

The best time with your friends is/was...

What can't you wait to do?

Favourite TV show?

Favourite food?

Favourite subject?

Favourite teacher?

Favourite video game?

Name:

Today's Date:

Date of Birth:

What 5 words describe you best?

What is your hobby or interest?

What do you want to be when you are an adult?

If you could have anything in the world what would it be?

What are the things you can't live without?

If you could be invisible for a day, what would you do?

What is the silliest thing you have ever done?

What do you like most about school?

What was your best ever school trip and why?

Your best school year memories so far are...

The best time with your friends is/was...

What can't you wait to do?

Favourite TV show?

Favourite food?

Favourite subject?

Favourite teacher?

Favourite video game?

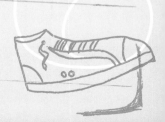

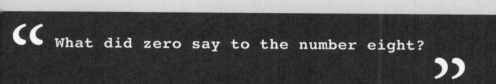
" What did zero say to the number eight? **"**

Nice belt.

Name:

Today's Date:

Date of Birth:

What 5 words describe you best?

What is your hobby or interest?

What do you want to be when you are an adult?

If you could have anything in the world what would it be?

What are the things you can't live without?

If you could be invisible for a day, what would you do?

What is the silliest thing you have ever done?

What do you like most about school?

What was your best ever school trip and why?

Your best school year memories so far are...

The best time with your friends is/was...

What can't you wait to do?

Favourite TV show?

Favourite food?

Favourite subject?

Favourite teacher?

Favourite video game?

Name:

Today's Date:

Date of Birth:

What 5 words describe you best?

What is your hobby or interest?

What do you want to be when you are an adult?

If you could have anything in the world what would it be?

What are the things you can't live without?

If you could be invisible for a day, what would you do?

YOU

What is the silliest thing you have ever done?

What do you like most about school?

What was your best ever school trip
and why?

Your best school year memories so far are...

The best time with your friends is/was...

What can't you wait to do?

Favourite TV show?

Favourite food?

Favourite subject?

Favourite teacher?

Favourite video game?

Name:

Today's Date:

Date of Birth:

What 5 words describe you best?

What is your hobby or interest?

What do you want to be when you are an adult?

If you could have anything in the world what would it be?

What are the things you can't live without?

If you could be invisible for a day, what would you do?

What is the silliest thing you have ever done?

What do you like most about school?

What was your best ever school trip and why?

yes!

Your best school year memories so far are...

The best time with your friends is/was...

What can't you wait to do?

Favourite TV show?

Favourite food?

Favourite subject?

Favourite teacher?

Favourite video game?

Name:

Today's Date:

Date of Birth:

What 5 words describe you best?

What is your hobby or interest?

What do you want to be when you are an adult?

If you could have anything in the world what would it be?

What are the things you can't live without?

If you could be invisible for a day, what would you do?

What is the silliest thing you have ever done?

What do you like most about school?

What was your best ever school trip and why?

Your best school year memories so far are...

The best time with your friends is/was...

What can't you wait to do?

Favourite TV show?

Favourite food?

Favourite subject?

Favourite teacher?

Favourite video game?

" What stays in the corner but travels around the world? **"**

Name:

Today's Date:

Date of Birth:

What 5 words describe you best?

What is your hobby or interest?

What do you want to be when you are an adult?

If you could have anything in the world what would it be?

What are the things you can't live without?

If you could be invisible for a day, what would you do?

What is the silliest thing you have ever done?

What do you like most about school?

What was your best ever school trip and why?

Your best school year memories so far are...

The best time with your friends is/was...

What can't you wait to do?

Favourite TV show?

Favourite food?

Favourite subject?

Favourite teacher?

Favourite video game?

AMAZE!

Name: _____

Today's Date: _____

Date of Birth: _____

What 5 words describe you best?

ABC

123

What is your hobby or interest?

What do you want to be when you are an adult?

If you could have anything in the world what would it be?

What are the things you can't live without?

If you could be invisible for a day, what would you do?

OMG! ☆

What is the silliest thing you have ever done?

What do you like most about school?

What was your best ever school trip and why?

Your best school year memories so far are...

The best time with your friends is/was...

What can't you wait to do?

Favourite TV show?

Favourite food?

Favourite subject?

Favourite teacher?

Favourite video game?

WOO HOO!

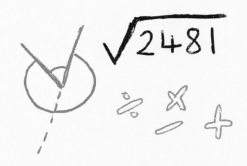

$$\sqrt{2481}$$

“ Neither, it's best to write with a pen! ”

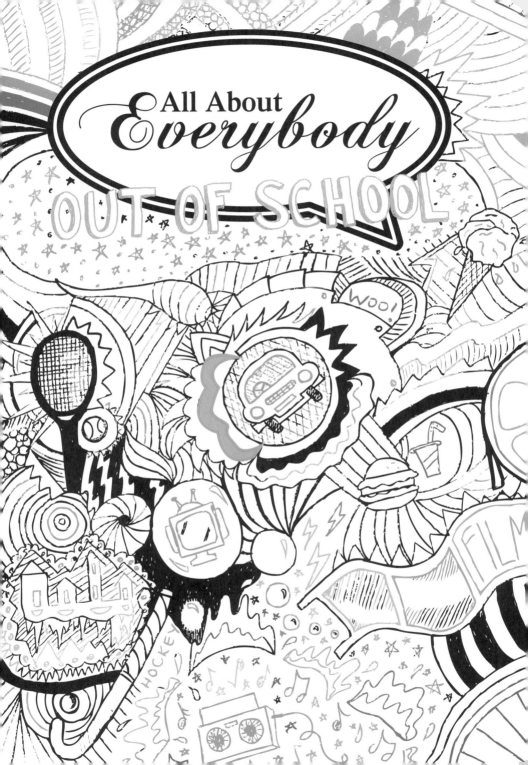

Name:

Today's Date:

Date of Birth:

What 5 words describe you best?

What is your hobby or interest?

What do you want to be when you are an adult?

If you could have anything in the world what would it be?

What are the things you can't live without?

If you could be invisible for a day, what would you do?

What is the silliest thing you have ever done?

What is the hardest thing you have ever done?

Where would you like to go that you haven't been before?

Your best memory so far is...

The best time with your friends is/was...

What can't you wait to do?

Favourite sport?

Favourite food?

Favourite TV show?

Favourite video game?

Favourite book?

Name:

Today's Date:

Date of Birth:

TWEET
TWEET

What 5 words describe you best?

What is your hobby or interest?

What do you want to be when you are an adult?

If you could have anything in the world what would it be?

What are the things you can't live without?

If you could be invisible for a day, what would you do?

What is the silliest thing you have ever done?

What is the hardest thing you have ever done?

Where would you like to go that you haven't been before?

Your best memory so far is...

The best time with your friends is/was...

What can't you wait to do?

Favourite sport?

Favourite food?

Favourite TV show?

Favourite video game?

Favourite book?

" Why did the jelly wobble?
"

((Because it saw the milk shake! **))**

Name:

Today's Date:

Date of Birth:

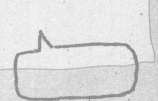

What 5 words describe you best?

What is your hobby or interest?

What do you want to be when you are an adult?

If you could have anything in the world what would it be?

What are the things you can't live without?

If you could be invisible for a day, what would you do?

What is the silliest thing you have ever done?

What is the hardest thing you have ever done?

Where would you like to go that you haven't been before?

Your best memory so far is...

The best time with your friends is/was...

What can't you wait to do?

Favourite sport?
Favourite food?
Favourite TV show?
Favourite video game?
Favourite book?

YES!

Name:

Today's Date:

Date of Birth:

What 5 words describe you best?

What is your hobby or interest?

What do you want to be when you are an adult?

If you could have anything in the world what would it be?

What are the things you can't live without?

If you could be invisible for a day, what would you do?

What is the silliest thing you have ever done?

What is the hardest thing you have ever done?

Where would you like to go that you haven't been before?

Your best memory so far is...

The best time with your friends is/was...

What can't you wait to do?

Favourite sport?

Favourite food?

Favourite TV show?

Favourite video game?

Favourite book?

If I had seven oranges in one hand and eight oranges in the other, what would I have?

Big hands!

Name:

Today's Date:

Date of Birth:

HI!

What 5 words describe you best?

What is your hobby or interest?

What do you want to be when you are an adult?

If you could have anything in the world what would it be?

What are the things you can't live without?

If you could be invisible for a day, what would you do?

What is the silliest thing you have ever done?

What is the hardest thing you have ever done?

Where would you like to go that you haven't been before?

Your best memory so far is...

The best time with your friends is/was...

What can't you wait to do?

Favourite sport?

Favourite food?

Favourite TV show?

Favourite video game?

Favourite book?

Name:

Today's Date:

Date of Birth:

What 5 words describe you best?

What is your hobby or interest?

What do you want to be when you are an adult?

If you could have anything in the world what would it be?

What are the things you can't live without?

If you could be invisible for a day, what would you do?

What is the silliest thing you have ever done?

What is the hardest thing you have ever done?

Where would you like to go that you haven't been before?

Your best memory so far is...

The best time with your friends is/was...

What can't you wait to do?

Favourite sport?

Favourite food?

Favourite TV show?

Favourite video game?

Favourite book?

" Because he had no-body to go with. "

Name:

Today's Date:

Date of Birth:

What 5 words describe you best?

What is your hobby or interest?

What do you want to be when you are an adult?

If you could have anything in the world what would it be?

What are the things you can't live without?

If you could be invisible for a day, what would you do?

What is the silliest thing you have ever done?

What is the hardest thing you have ever done?

Where would you like to go that you haven't been before?

Your best memory so far is...

The best time with your friends is/was...

What can't you wait to do?

Favourite sport?

Favourite food?

Favourite TV show?

Favourite video game?

Favourite book?

Name:

Today's Date:

Date of Birth:

What 5 words describe you best?

What is your hobby or interest?

What do you want to be when you are an adult?

If you could have anything in the world what would it be?

What are the things you can't live without?

If you could be invisible for a day, what would you do?

AWESOME

What is the silliest thing you have ever done?

What is the hardest thing you have ever done?

Where would you like to go that you haven't been before?

Your best memory so far is...

The best time with your friends is/was...

What can't you wait to do?

Favourite sport?

Favourite food?

Favourite TV show?

Favourite video game?

Favourite book?

**   ❝** What musical key do cows sing in? **❞**

“ Beef flat (Bb). **”**

Name:

Today's Date:

Date of Birth:

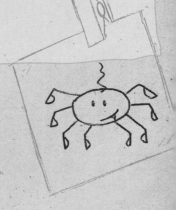

What 5 words describe you best?

What is your hobby or interest?

What do you want to be when you are an adult?

If you could have anything in the world what would it be?

What are the things you can't live without?

If you could be invisible for a day, what would you do?

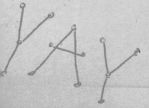

_TEXT ME

What is the silliest thing you have ever done?

What is the hardest thing you have ever done?

Where would you like to go that you haven't been before?

Your best memory so far is...

The best time with your friends is/was...

What can't you wait to do?

Favourite sport?

Favourite food?

Favourite TV show?

Favourite video game?

Favourite book?

Name:

Today's Date:

Date of Birth:

What 5 words describe you best?

What is your hobby or interest?

What do you want to be when you are an adult?

If you could have anything in the world what would it be?

What are the things you can't live without?

If you could be invisible for a day, what would you do?

What is the silliest thing you have ever done?

What is the hardest thing you have ever done?

Where would you like to go that you haven't been before?

Your best memory so far is...

The best time with your friends is/was...

What can't you wait to do?

Favourite sport?

Favourite food?

Favourite TV show?

Favourite video game?

Favourite book?

DOCTOR: Tell him I can't see him now. Next.

Name:

Today's Date:

Date of Birth:

What 5 words describe you best?

What is your hobby or interest?

What do you want to be when you are an adult?

If you could have anything in the world what would it be?

What are the things you can't live without?

If you could be invisible for a day, what would you do?

What is the silliest thing you have ever done?

What is the hardest thing you have ever done?

Where would you like to go that you haven't been before?

Your best memory so far is...

The best time with your friends is/was...

What can't you wait to do?

Favourite sport?

Favourite food?

Favourite TV show?

Favourite video game?

Favourite book?

Name:

Today's Date:

Date of Birth:

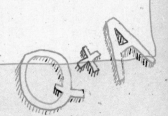

What 5 words describe you best?

What is your hobby or interest?

What do you want to be when you are an adult?

If you could have anything in the world what would it be?

What are the things you can't live without?

If you could be invisible for a day, what would you do?

What is the silliest thing you have ever done?

What is the hardest thing you have ever done?

Where would you like to go that you haven't been before?

Your best memory so far is...

The best time with your friends is/was...

What can't you wait to do?

Favourite sport?

Favourite food?

Favourite TV show?

Favourite video game?

Favourite book?

PARTY TIME!

Name:

Today's Date:

Date of Birth:

What 5 words describe you best?

What is your hobby or interest?

What do you want to be when you are an adult?

If you could have anything in the world what would it be?

What are the things you can't live without?

If you could be invisible for a day, what would you do?

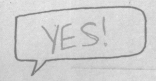

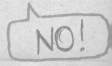

What is the silliest thing you have ever done?

What is the hardest thing you have ever done?

Where would you like to go that you haven't been before?

Your best memory so far is...

The best time with your friends is/was...

What can't you wait to do?

Favourite sport?

Favourite food?

Favourite TV show?

Favourite video game?

Favourite book?

Name:

Today's Date:

Date of Birth:

What 5 words describe you best?

What is your hobby or interest?

What do you want to be when you are an adult?

If you could have anything in the world what would it be?

What are the things you can't live without?

If you could be invisible for a day, what would you do?

What is the silliest thing you have ever done?

What is the hardest thing you have ever done?

Where would you like to go that you haven't been before?

Your best memory so far is...

The best time with your friends is/was...

What can't you wait to do?

Favourite sport?

Favourite food?

Favourite TV show?

Favourite video game?

Favourite book?

“ A child walked into a shop... ”

Ouch!

DATE	EVENT

>> SPECIAL DATES & EVENTS

DATE	EVENT

DATE	EVENT

>> SPECIAL DATES & EVENTS

DATE	EVENT

	YEAR	YEAR ....
Favourite food?	....	....
Favourite drink?	....	....
Favourite TV series?	....	....
Favourite movie?	....	....
Favourite music artist?	....	....
Favourite celebrity?	....	....
Favourite colour?	....	....
Favourite time of day?	....	....
Favourite sport?	....	....
Favourite class?	....	....
Favourite teacher?	....	....
Favourite subject?	....	....
Favourite place?	....	....

YEAR ....

....
....
....
....
....
....
....
....
....
....
....
....
....

YEAR ....

....
....
....
....
....
....
....
....
....
....
....
....
....

YEAR ....

....
....
....
....
....
....
....
....
....
....
....
....
....

DON'T FORGET!

ALL ABOUT EVERYBODY

Other books in the range include:

All About Everybody in my life

All About Everybody in my family

All About Everybody at our wedding

All About Everybody on my special birthday

Available from www.allabouteverybody.com